TRADE AND COLLECT

TAX DISCS

First Edition © 2006

Published by: Collecticus, P.O.Box 100, Devizes, Wiltshire, SN10 4TE

Acknowledgements:
DVLA, D.J. Le Breton, David Clark

Crown Copyright material by kind permission of
Her Majesty's Stationery Office

Typeset, make-up and printing; Hartley Publications, 49 Lancaster Road, Bowerhill Trading Estate, Melksham, Wiltshire, SN12 6SS

Introduction

Fortunately, not many people have discovered the fascination of expired tax discs otherwise the rare discs would be in far more demand than they are now and this hobby would be far more expensive to indulge in.

The trade in expired vehicle tax discs is relatively new but is rapidly gaining momentum.

Collectors are continually looking for excellent examples and there lies a problem. Tax discs were normally purchased for the purpose of being displayed on a vehicle and were therefore subject to rough handling, sunlight fading, dampness etc... Good examples are therefore not always easy to find. Values are governed by the condition as well as the rarity. However, a collector looking to fill a gap is likely to welcome an elusive disc in any condition whatsoever. Upgrading can come later. And that is a reason why trading activity is increasing.

Elite Registrations (one of Britain's best known dealers in personalised car registration numbers) are believed to be the innovators of the commercial aspect of the hobby (known as velology).

The word velology is derived from Vehicle Excise Licence (vel) + ology. A collector is known as a velologist. As yet, the words are not to be found in the English Dictionary.

How much a tax disc is worth is normally decided by supply and demand. However, some kind of guidance has to be helpful and you will therefore find over 200 different discs individually priced on page 92. These are actual asking prices and all discs are offered for sale (subject to availability).

To set up as a trader, it would help if you enjoy the subject and acquire an in-depth knowledge. Then it's a case of speculating. If interest continues to grow then inevitably values will climb. However, it has to be said that most people would class you as a brave speculator if you invest heavily at this stage.

There are countless different examples of discs and it really is fascinating to discover how they have evolved since the first issues back in 1921.

It's a safe bet that the majority of motorists failed to realise that an expired disc would end up being worth more than the original cost, albeit 50 years or so later. For example a 1947 tax disc for a motorcycle cost about £1. Now, the disc (in good condition) could fetch more than ten times the original cost.

The message now is to make sure that you keep your tax disc in tip-top condition whilst being displayed on your vehicle, and once the disc has expired don't throw it away !

1921

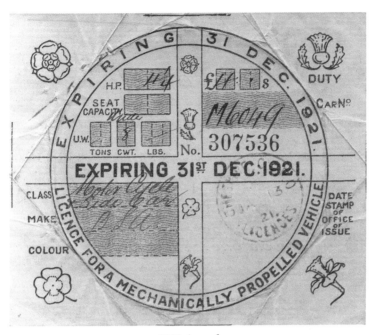

1921 Annual

Although vehicle taxation had been in place for many years, it wasn't until the implementation of the Finance Act 1920 that the issuing and displaying of tax discs became a legal requirement and from the 1st January 1921 motorists were obliged to display a disc on the vehicle. At the same time, petrol tax was abolished and the collection of vehicle duty was no longer the responsibility of HM Customs & Excise. Motorists were given two options, either to buy a 'quarterly' or an 'annual' disc.

The first of the quarterly discs was set to expire to coincide with the Spring Equinox 24th March, rather than 31st March, yet the cost was no different to the remaining three quarters, expiring 30th June (Summer Solstice), 30th September (Autumn Equinox) and then 31st December (Winter Solstice). Although it has to be noted that 31st December is only an approximate date for the Winter Solstice (generally around 22nd December).

The very first expiry date. March 1921 quarterly

The discs were produced on plain paper and had no perforation to separate the disc from the selvedge (outer margins).

The size of the tax disc was prescribed within the Regulations and the size has largely remained the same to this day.

Quite interestingly it would appear that the Authorities may not have complied with the legal requirements of the legislation. The wording of the requirement reads; "the licence will be a card of stout paper". The discs were in fact pieces of paper that by no stretch of the imagination could be described as 'card' or 'stout paper'.

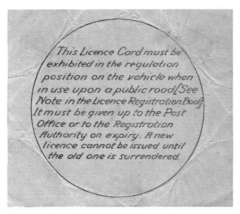

Reverse of the 1921 annual disc

The text on the reverse side of the original disc was simple. Note: no refund for the surrender of the disc prior to the expiry date.

1922

The quarterly discs of 1922

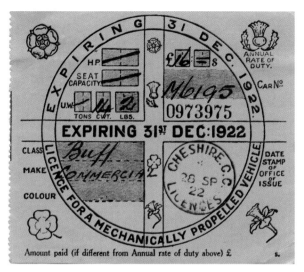

1922 annual

This was the only annual disc ever to be printed with identical colouring of the previous year's disc.

1923

It soon dawned on the Authorities that it was rather inconvenient to force motorists to hand-in the old disc before taking out a new one. It meant that the vehicle could not be used on the public highway during the exchange period, otherwise the motorist would be liable to a penalty for non-display.

However, if the licence was renewed at a Post Office, the old disc still had to be surrendered.

Motorists were now instructed to destroy expired tax discs in their possession. Presumably, this is the reason why discs from 1921 – 1924 are quite hard to find today.

1923 annual

The printing of discs was improved using background intaglio (design in relief), together with a coloured vertical bar.

This Licence Card must be exhibited in the regulation position on the vehicle when in use upon a public road (See Note in the Licence Registration Book). It must be destroyed on expiry unless renewed at a Post Office when it must be surrendered.

1923 annual reverse

1924

The Finance Act 1924 (Section 18) introduced refunds for surrendered licences for each complete month of the unexpired period of the currency of the disc.

The information relating to the refunds was not specified on the reverse of discs until the 1926 expiry dates.

It was decided to remove the notice on the reverse of the discs from the last quarter of 1924. The notice was replaced with commercial advertising. The December quarterly carried an advertisement for three booklets on the subject of lubrication, published by Price's Motor Oils.

1924 annual reverse

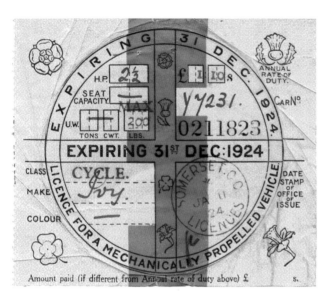

1924 annual

1925

Advertising on the reverse of discs was in full swing, with Shell Motor Oils poaching three of the quarterlies and the annual. Presumably advertising was allocated to motor-related companies willing to pay the most. The June quarterly carried an advertisement for Jeavons Spring Gaiters.

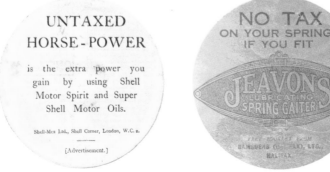

1926

Advertising was dropped from the reverse of the disc and was never re-introduced.

A new notice appeared on the reverse, specifying the facility to claim a refund for unexpired duty.

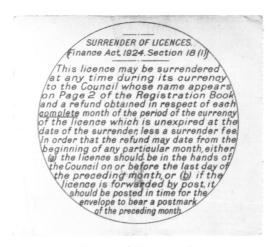

Reverse of 1926 annual

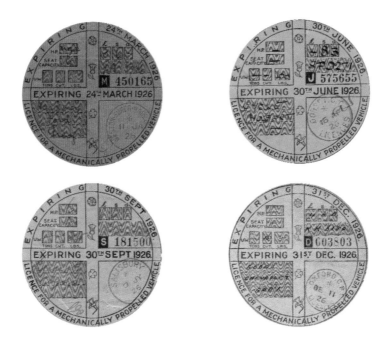

The letter prefixing the serial number of the disc was reversed out in a box. M for March etc…

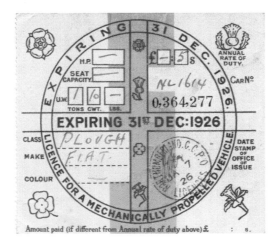

1927

Whilst the format of the quarterly discs remained unchanged, the colour bar for the annual disc (horizontal for this year) had three variations to the theme. Firstly, grey and purple, secondly, all green, and thirdly, all purple.

1928

The March quarterly kept the same format but the June quarterly saw a significant change to the prefix letter for the serial number. It was moved to the centre margin, thereby providing more space for the serial number.

1929

1930

1931

1932

The quarterly disc format remained unchanged but the annual disc changed from a coloured vertical bar to a horizontal bar and heralded the beginning of a rotation of variations to the coloured bars.

1932 Annual disc with the selvedge intact.

1933

1934

1935

The 'cross' colour bar was introduced for the first time.

1936

1937

1938

Two significant changes this year, the most important being the introduction of perforations to the circumference of the disc, making it much easier to separate the margin (selvedge). All of the quarterly discs also had perforations. The second change was the colour bar. A diagonal bar, was introduced. This was the last of the variety of bars.

1939

A large 'F' was printed on discs allocated to agricultural vehicles. They became known as 'Farmers Discs'.

1940

1941

1942

Only the Annual and the March quarterly retained perforations. From the June quarterly onwards (for the next ten years) discs were issued without perforations.

1943

1943 Annual

1943 Annual (Northern Ireland issue, with selvedge)

1944

1945

27

1946

1947

1948

1949

1950

EXPIRING 31 DEC.1950.

H.P.

SEAT CAPACITY.

U.W. TONS CWT. LBS.

£ 10 s. d.

BCN 968

0214144

EXPIRING 31ST DEC:1950.

PRIVATE
AUSTIN
BROWN

GATESHEAD C.B.C. 20 SP 50 LICENCES

FOR REFUNDS SEE CONDITIONS ON BACK OF LICENCE.

EXPIRING 31 DEC:1950. LICENCE FOR A MECHANICALLY PROPELLED VEHICLE

SURRENDER OF LICENCES

This licence may be surrendered at any time during its currency to the Council whose name appears on page 2 of the Registration Book and a refund obtained in respect of each **complete** month of the period of the currency of the licence which is unexpired at the date of the surrender. In order that the refund may date from the beginning of any particular month, either (a) the licence must be handed in at the Council's offices on or before the last day of the preceding month,* or (b) if the licence is sent by post, it must be posted before midnight on the last day of the month.* **Handing in on the first will not do.**

*NOTE. For a refund to be payable in respect of the month of April, the licence must be surrendered on or before the 24th March.

1951

A new design was introduced. Most significantly, the thistle, shamrock, daffodil and rose symbols were deleted from the discs. They were replaced in the vertical bar with the year in digits. The horizontal bar was increased in size, allowing the expiry date to be more prominent.

Perforations were also re-introduced.

1952

1952 Annual

The March quarterly witnessed a new 'light shade of yellow' paper used for the first time.

1953

The annual disc had two (subtle) variations. One had an entirely red vertical bar and the other had a predominantly orange bar with red in the top and bottom circumference margin.

1954

The Regulations clearly prescribe that the four quarterly discs should be of different colours and indeed this requirement had been religiously adhered to with colourful variations. So you may be surprised to find that, presumably as the result of a blunder, the December quarterly was the same colour as March.

This apparent blunder extended further with a quantity of the annuals being printed with the incorrect year (1953) and then requiring an overprint. Of course, when printing of these discs began, the year was actually 1953, and therefore a (feeble) excuse for the error. At least the colour scheme and position of the vertical colour bar were both correct.

And yet another anomaly occurred with a quantity of the December quarterlies having to be overprinted in red, blanking out the 24th March expiry date.

This year of issue therefore presents an opportunity for the speculator. Quite how many erroneous discs exist is unknown, however, the overprints are certainly more desirable, but unfortunately not uncommon. It therefore has to be a case of letting the market dictate the value and demand. Unquestionably, no serious collection should be void of the overprints.

1955

The colour variations for the quarterlies were surprisingly unimaginative and arguably defeated the object of having easily distinguishable different colours for the four expiry dates.

1956

1957

Another significant change of format and arguably a flaw in the design with the typeface size of the quarterly dates being significantly reduced.

The typeface size of the year was slightly increased (from the June quarterly onwards).

For the first time, the position of the issuing office handstamp was changed to a central position in the lower segment.

VEHICLES (EXCISE) ACT, 1949.

2172301

EXPIRING 31ST DECEMBER

UHK 290
BICYCLE
CYCLEMASTER

TONS	CWT.	CAP. OR H.P.	s.	s.	d.
		25cc	—	17	6

FOR REFUNDS SEE CONDITIONS ON BACK OF LICENCE.

19 57

ESSEX C.C.
*
9 JA
57
LICENCES

LICENCE FOR A MECHANICALLY PROPELLED VEHICLE

VEHICLES (EXCISE) ACT, 1949.

1035168

EXPIRING 31ST DECEMBER

582 FMH
PRIVATE
M.G.

TONS	CWT.	CAP. OR H.P.	s.	s.	d.
				12	10	0

FOR REFUNDS SEE CONDITIONS ON BACK OF LICENCE.

19 57

LONDON C.C.
1
1 JA
57
LICENCES

LICENCE FOR A MECHANICALLY PROPELLED VEHICLE

1958

1959

1960

This was the last year for the quarterly tax disc and in fact they were terminated with the disc expiring 30th September. From then onwards the minimum period of taxation changed from 3 months (quarterly) to 4 months. Therefore the fourth expiry date became January 1961.

The disc (shown below) expiring 31st December is the annual.

1961

January 1961

This significant change of format was introduced with discs expiring end of January 1961. Arguably, this remains the clearest format ever to be used.

SURRENDER OF LICENCES
Vehicles (Excise) Act, 1949, Section 12.

This licence may be surrendered at any time during its currency to the Council whose name appears on page 4 of the Registration Book and a refund obtained in respect of each **complete** month of the period of the currency of the licence which is unexpired at the date of the surrender. In order that the refund may date from the beginning of any particular month, either (*a*) the licence must be handed in at the Council's offices on or before the last day of the preceding month, or (*b*) if the licence is sent by post, it must be posted before midnight on the last day of the preceding month. **Handing in on the first will not do.**

Reverse of the January 1961 disc

The prefix letter of the serial number was abolished and replaced with a number between one and zero. January being allocated the number one and so on through to zero for October. Then, the months of November and December reverted to letters (N and D respectively).

It was now possible to take out an annual disc that would expire at the end of a month other than December. For example; a licence taken out for 12 months at the beginning of March 1961 would have an expiry date of February 1962.

Not that many owners of private motor cars would have noticed, the monthly cost of the licence reduced by threepence with the introduction of the 4 month period in 1961, although the cost of an annual disc remained the same.

1962

For security purposes (helping to prevent cut-and-paste deceptions) a repeat of the expiry date was added, in a tint, just below the centre of the disc.

1963

1964 - 1971

Welsh language variation

'Farmers' disc with Selvedge

Emergency discs were introduced for use when the supply of normal discs became restricted, because of postal strikes etc… The serial number was prefixed with the letter 'E'.

1972

February 1972 normal issue

February 1972 emergency issue

1973

1974

DVLC (Driver and Vehicle Licensing Centre) began operations at Swansea and started the conversion of existing vehicle records, from the manual record system managed by local Motor Taxation Offices, to a computerised system. New local offices were opened and called VROs (Vehicle Registration Offices).

Motor Taxation Offices remained open for business but were given notice of eventual closure whenever the task of converting records of all licensed vehicles had been completed.

A disc with a VRO or DVLC handstamp dated 1974 can be held in high regard.

A December 1974 disc (with selvedge) issued for a mobile crane.

1975

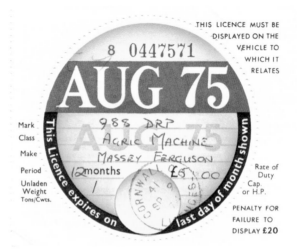

August 1975 with selvedge

November 1975 with selvedge

February 1975

February 1975 Emergency issue

September 1975

September 1975 Emergency issue

October 1975

October 1975 Emergency issue

1976

The production and issuing of emergency discs ceased.

The above is an early example of a disc with a DVLC, Swansea handstamp (issued in 1975)

1977

From October, the expiry date was digitalised, although some offices continued issuing the existing style.

Where the duty had been printed on the new style disc specifying the old rate (£14.65 instead of £18.35), the new rate was 'rubber stamped' on.

The reverse of the disc was changed to include a reference to DVLC.

REFUND OF DUTY

Vehicles (Excise) Act, 1971.

This licence may be surrendered at any time during its currency to the Council with which the vehicle is registered and a refund obtained in respect of each **complete** month of the period of the currency of the licence which is unexpired at the date of the surrender. In order that the refund may date from the beginning of any particular month, either (a) the licence must be handed in at the Council's offices on or before the last day of the preceding month, or (b) if the licence is sent by post, it must be posted before midnight on the last day of the preceding month. **Handing in on the first will not do.**

Reverse of October 1977 (old style)

REFUND OF DUTY

This licence may be surrendered at any time for a refund of duty for each complete month left to run. A month will only count for refund if the licence is handed in or put in the post **on or before the last day of the preceding month.**

To claim a refund take or post the licence to the Council shown in the Registration Book (VE60) or if the vehicle has a Registration Document (V5) post the licence to the Driver and Vehicle Licensing Centre, **SWANSEA SA99 1AL** or hand it in at any Local Vehicle Licensing Office.

Reverse of October 1977 (new style)

58

1978

The changeover from Motor Taxation Offices to DVLC, Swansea was largely completed.

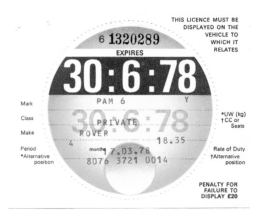

THIS LICENCE MUST BE
DISPLAYED ON THE
VEHICLE TO
WHICH IT
RELATES

6 1320289

EXPIRES

30:6:78

Mark

PAM 6

Class

•UW (kg)
†CC or
Seats

Make

PRIVATE
ROVER

Period
•Alternative
position

4   months   7.03.78   18.35
8076 3721 0014

Rate of Duty
†Alternative
position

PENALTY FOR
FAILURE TO
DISPLAY £20

June 1978 with selvedge

7 0023553
EXPIRES
31:7:78
BJX 854S
PRIVATE
FORD
12   months   50.00
28.07.77
7209 3341 0222

8 2832117
EXPIRES
31:8:78
FPX 5H
PRIVATE
FORD
4   months   18.35
27.04.78
8117 3672 0106

9 1406174
EXPIRES
30:9:78
806 B
TRIUMPH
4   months   7.35
5.08.78
8227 3601 0314

0 1738569
EXPIRES
31:10:78
1 VVW
PRIVATE
WOL SELEY
£50
12   months

N 0045207
EXPIRES
30:11:78
XUG 248S
PRIVATE
AUSTIN
12   months   50.00
23.11.77
7327 3363 0061

0 3612696
EXPIRES
31:12:78
EHJ 271C
PRIVATE
TRIUMPH
4   months   18.35
8251 3592 0454

1979

A digit (representing the last number in the year) was added to the top left of the selvedge. The first number used being '9' representing 1979.

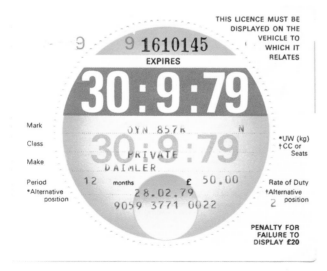

1980

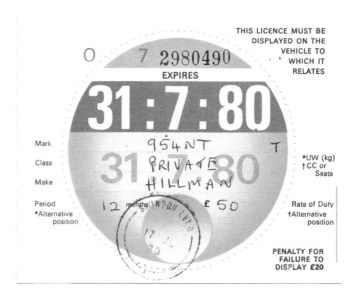

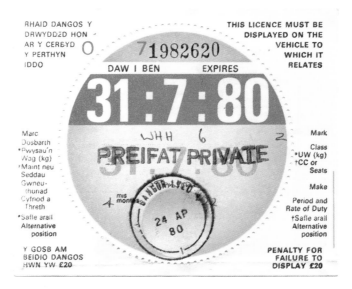

Welsh issue with selvedge

1981

Periods of 4 months of licensing ceased. Motorists now had only two options, '6 months' or '12 months'.

Penalty for failure to display a tax disc, rose from £20 to £50.

1982

1 0940232
EXPIRES
31:1:82
EJM 969V   3
PRIVATE
ROVER
12   months   £50.00
1041 3661 0147

2 3184686
EXPIRES
28:2:82
383 FFD   N
6 months   38·50
BRIDGWATER
8 SP
81
SOMERSET

3 2123984
EXPIRES
31:3:82
KLP 646T   0/0
PRIVATE
FORD
6 months   £38.50

4 1233675
EXPIRES
30:4:82
EHJ 271C
PRIVATE
TRIUMPH
6 months   £8.50
1 NO
81

5 1483493
EXPIRES
31:5:82
EFL 156L   O
Private Rover
Ford
12 months   £70.00

6 1783243
EXPIRES
30:6:82
AHU 14cV   *
PRIVATE
LEYLAND
months   .01.82   £38.50
2012 3771 0008

7 0835208
EXPIRES
31:7:82
EUT 169T   *
PRIVATE
ROLLS ROYCE
12   70.00
months 27.08.81£
1239 3413 0124

8 1718969
EXPIRES
31:8:82
SNJ 184N   P
WORKS TRUCK
THWAITES
12 months   £12·00
81
SUSSEX

9 1706928
EXPIRES
30:9:82
YKN 197 J   7
GOODS 5581·5
ERE
12 months   £515

O 2808354
EXPIRES
31:10:82
EHJ 271C   G
PRIVATE
TRIUMPH
6 months   £44

N 0134393
EXPIRES
30:11:82
215 PF   *
PRIVATE
BMW
12 months   £70.00
8.12.8f
1342 3552 0373

D 2949644
EXPIRES
31:12:82
231 JFK   /
PRIVATE
AUSTIN   848cc
6 months   £44
BATH
N
JY
15
82

64

1983 - 1986

1987

Another significant change of design (to help improve security), from the October disc onwards. A new (and slightly smaller) typeface was used for the expiry date. Wavy lines (made up with the repeated letters 'DVLC') were also added and most significantly the discs were embossed with the repeated letters 'DVLC' across the top (between the serial number and the word 'expires'). The perforations were interspersed in three places with elliptical holes and a further two in the body of the disc (one above each of the date colons).

The penalty for failure to display a tax disc increased from £50 to £100.

5 0334570
EXPIRES
31:5:87
GHY 530 T
PLG 31:5:87
JAGUAR
12 months £100.00

60232471
EXPIRES
30:6:87
A971 YUV (2)
PLG 30:6:87
Mercedes
6 months £65.00

7 0470682
EXPIRES
31:7:87
JHR 141 B   L
BICYCLE   49CC
Mobylette
12 months £10-

8 0327593
EXPIRES
31:8:87
UHT 40E Y   T
PLG 31:8:87
BMW
6 months £55.00

9 1164838
EXPIRES
30:9:87
324 NOR M
30:9:87
WOLSELEY
12 months £100.00

0 3119695
EXPIRES
31:10:87
WRC 441   M
PLG 31:10:87
VOLKSWAGEN
6 mths £55.00

N0367907
EXPIRES
30:11:87
XHR 253A   2
PLG 30:11:87
ROVER
12 mths £100-

D 0432219
EXPIRES
31:12:87
JHR 152B   7
PLG 31:12:87
FORD
12 mths £100.00

1988

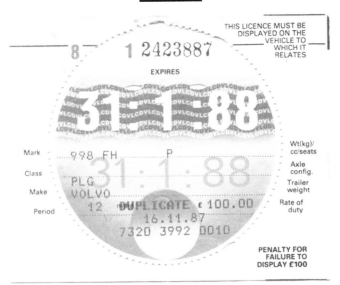

1989

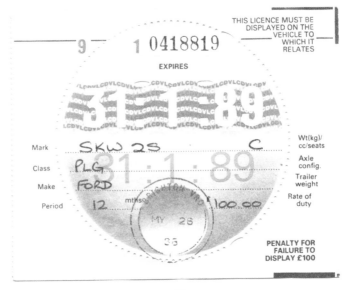

1990

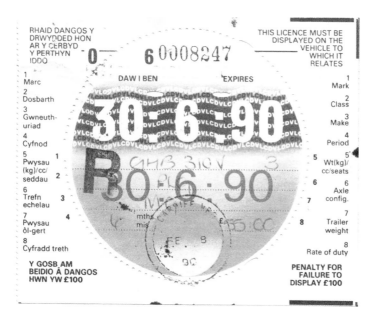

Welsh Variation

1991

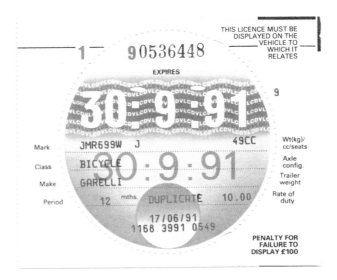

Handstamps at VRO's were being gradually phased out. Machines printed the vehicle information on each disc.

The printer used elite typeface (12 characters per linear inch).

The last line (bottom segment of the disc) carried a structured code split into three groups of digits.

The example shown above was structured as follows:-

The first group of digits 1168, represents '1' for 1991, '168' for the 168th day of the year. The second group of digits 3991 is made up of '399' for the VRO's unique reference code and '1' for the machine no.1 in the office. The third group of digits 0549 indicates that this is the 549th disc to be issued by the VRO that day.

1992

1 0402045

2 0435826

3 1647510

4 3829032

5 0569977

6 0408681

7 0427508

8 0224346

9 1330933

0 0649162

N 0593566

D 0288831

1993

Another significant change of design from March onwards.

For the first time, the day of the month of expiry was removed from the disc. This allowed more space to increase the size of the typeface for the month and year, thus making it considerably easier to read from a distance.

The wavy line was changed from the repeated letters 'DVLC' to the repeated word 'expires'. A grey tint was added either side of a central column, creating a distinctive band.

D 029504G

THIS LICENCE MUST BE
DISPLAYED ON THE
VEHICLE TO
WHICH IT
RELATES

EXPIRES

12 93

10

31 : 12 : 93

		Wt(kg)/
Mark	J689 LHR E	cc/seats 49CC
Class	BICYCLE	Axle config.
Make	JAWA	Trailer weight
Period	12 mths. REPLACED £ 15.00	Rate of duty

30/07/93
3211 3772 0105

PENALTY FOR
FAILURE TO
DISPLAY £100

REFUND OF DUTY

This licence may be surrendered
at any time for a refund of duty for
each complete month left to run. A month
will only count for refund if the licence is
handed in or put in the post **on or before the
last day of the preceding month.**

To claim a refund send your application and the
licence to the Driver and Vehicle Licensing Centre
SWANSEA SA99 1AL or hand them in
at any Vehicle Registration Office. Refund
application forms (V14) may be obtained from
any Vehicle Registration Office or
main post offices.

Reverse of the December 1993 disc

1994

The embossed repeated letters 'DVLC' running across the top of the disc were changed to 'DVLA' to correspond with the Agency status of the DVLC. The Driver & Vehicle Licensing Agency. However, the reverse of the disc retained reference to 'DVLC' and remained so for a further eight years.

The positions of the elliptical holes around the perforations were changed.

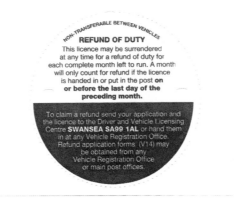

1995

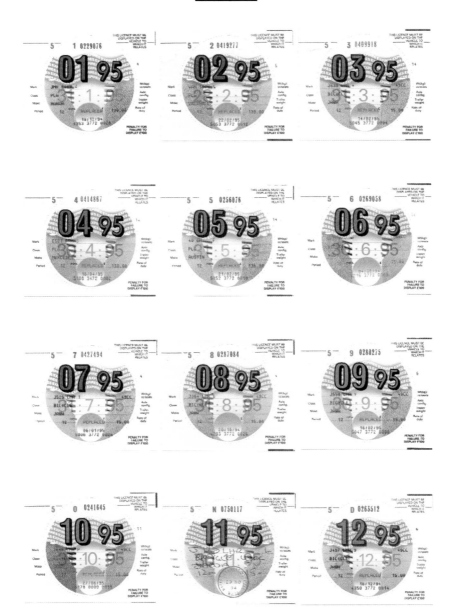

1996

1997

1998

Penalty for failure to display increased from £100 to £200

1999

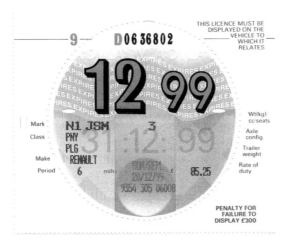

The last expiry date of the twentieth century

2000

The first expiry date of the new century. The novelty of the printed date 01 : 00 makes this particular issue a 'must' for collectors but is not a rarity.

2001

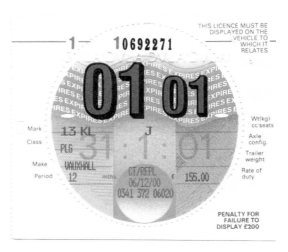

2002

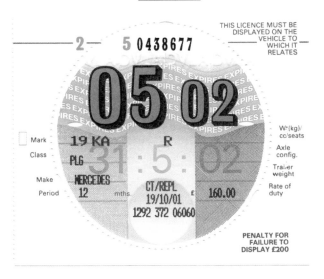

Reference on the reverse of the disc, to the Driver and Vehicle Licensing **Centre** was eventually dropped and replaced with the word **Agency**

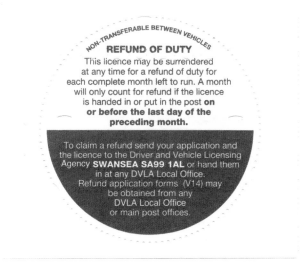

2003

Another significant change of style was introduced, from October onwards, in a further bid to combat fraudulent reproduction of discs. New security features (including a barcode) were introduced. The date colour was changed to gold on black, albeit rather controversially, because they were not easy to read from a distance.

The last date of the month was reintroduced to the wavy line section.

The prefix of the serial number of the disc was changed to the representative number of the month. 10 was used for October and so on.

Existing style discs continued to also be produced throughout the entire year.

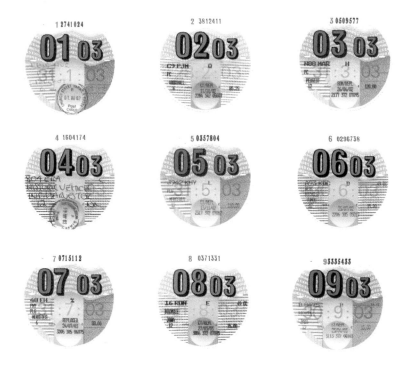

O 0395715

10 03
K70 JMR L 49 CC
BICYCLE
JAWA
12 mths. CT/REPL £ 15.00
05/09/03
3248 372 09009

10 4815359 3

31 10 03
CX51 NCV / L £ 15.00
EASY RIDER BEIC
49 CC 28/10/03 BICYCLE
12 3301 391 01130
CT/REPL

N 3806526

11 03
ANTRYN
30·11·03
6 mths.
POST OFFICE 16 JU 03 TROWBRIDGE D E WILTS

11 8231823 4

30 11 03
MLZ4236 /B £ 15.00
HONDA BICYCLE
49CC 21/10/03
12 11/25 CTS
N8231823

D 0562535

12 03
JW 4206 1 49 CC
BICYCLE
JAWA
12 mths. CT/REPL £ 15.00
19/09/03
3262 372 01029

12 5075434 4

31 12 03
P32 WFE / 2 £ 90.75
SUBARU PLG
29/12/03
6 3363 348 05042
CT/REPL

2004

Old style discs were eventually phased out after the expiry of the August licence.

50571406

05 6072311 3

6 1563618

06 8117554 0

70002216

07 4259545 4

8 0604922

08 4113755 4

0904

09 0597480 1

EXPIRES 30 09 04

HW 333 / R £ 15.00

Mark — Rate of duty

Make — JAVA — BICYCLE / — Class

Wt(kg)/cc/seats — 49 CC — 20/02/04 — Trailer weight

Period — 12 — 4051 372 00025 — CLASS

MAXIMUM PENALTY FOR FAILURE TO DISPLAY £200

0904

10 0594272 2

EXPIRES 31 10 04

K'70 JMR / L £ 15.00

Mark — Rate of duty

Make — JAVA — BICYCLE / — Class

Wt(kg)/cc/seats — 49 CC — 23/10/03 — Trailer weight

Period — 12 — 5296 372 00068

MAXIMUM PENALTY FOR FAILURE TO DISPLAY £200

0904

11 0492648 5

EXPIRES 30 11 04

1CUC /G £ 125.00

Mark — Rate of duty

Make — PEUGEOT — PC — Class

Wt(kg)/cc/seats — 07/05/04 — Trailer weight

Period — 12 — 4428 330 004040

MAXIMUM PENALTY FOR FAILURE TO DISPLAY £200

0904

12 0593308 3

EXPIRES 31 12 04

JW 4206 / 1 £ 15.00

Mark — Rate of duty

Make — JAVA — BICYCLE / — Class

Wt(kg)/cc/seats — 49 CC — 15/12/03 — Trailer weight

Period — 12 — 5369 372 00012

MAXIMUM PENALTY FOR FAILURE TO DISPLAY £200

2005

Yet another change started taking effect with the February expiry date. The gold on black 'date' colour was reversed to black on gold (making the discs easier to read from a distance).

2006

Disc expiring January 2006

86

Original Registration Authorities responsible for the issuing of vehicle tax discs.

Index Mark	Registering County or Boro' Council	Index Mark	Registering County or Boro' Council	Index Mark	Registering County or Boro' Council	Index Mark	Registering County or Boro' Council
A	London (Also LC)	CI	Queen's County	EW	Huntingdonshire	L	Glamorganshire
AA	Southampton (CC)	CJ	Herefordshire	EX	Great Yarmouth	LI	West Meath
AB	Worcestershire	CK	Preston	EY	Anglesey	LS	Selkirk
AC	Warwickshire	CL	Norwich	F	Essex	M	Cheshire
AD	Gloucestershire	CM	Birkenhead	FA	Burton-On-Trent	ML	Wexford
AE	Bristol	CN	Gateshead	FB	Bath	MS	Stirling
AF	Cornwall	CO	Plymouth	FC	Oxford	N	Manchester
AH	Norfolk	CP	Halifax	FD	Dudley	NI	Wicklow
AI	Meath	CR	Southampton (Boro)	FE	Lincoln	NS	Sutherland
AJ	Yorkshire (NR)	CT	Kesteven, Lincolnshire	FF	Merionethshire	O	Birmingham
AK	Bradford (Yorks)	CU	South Shields	FH	Gloucester	OI	Belfast
AL	Nottinghamshire	CW	Burnley	FI	Tipperary (NR)	OS	Wigtown
AM	Wiltshire	CX	Huddersfield	FJ	Exeter	P	Surrey
AN	West Ham	CY	Swansea	FK	Worcester	PI	Cork (Borough)
AO	Cumberland	D	Kent	FL	Peterborough	PS	Shetland
AP	Sussex East	DA	Wolverhampton	FM	Chester	R	Derbyshire
AR	Hertfordshire	DB	Stockport	FN	Canterbury	RI	Dublin
AS	Nairn	DC	Middlesbrough	FO	Radnorshire	RS	Aberdeen (Town C)
AT	Kingston-On-Hull	DE	Pembrokeshire	FP	Rutlandshire	S	Edinburgh (TC)
AU	Nottingham	DF	North'mpt'n (Also NH)	FR	Blackpool	SA	Aberdeen (County)
AW	Shropshire	DH	Walsall	FT	Tynemouth	SB	Argyll
AX	Monmouthshire	DI	Roscommon	FX	Dorsetshire	SD	Ayr
AY	Leicestershire	DJ	St Helens	FY	Southport	SE	Banff
B	Lancashire	DK	Rochdale	G	Glasgow Town C	SH	Berwick
BA	Salford	DL	Isle Of Wight	H	Middlesex	SJ	Bute
BB	Newctle-On-Tyne	DM	Flintshire	HI	Tipperary (SR)	SK	Caithness
BS	Leicester	DN	York	HS	Renfrew	SL	Clackmannan
BD	Northamptonshire	DO	Holland, Lincolnshire	IA	Antrim	SM	Dumfries
BE	Lindsey, Lincs	DP	Reading	IB	Armagh	SN	Dumbarton
BF	Dorsetshire	DR	Devonport	IC	Carlow	S	Elgiu
BH	Buckinghamshire	DS	Peebles	ID	Cavan	SP	Fife
BI	Monaghan	DU	Coventry	IE	Clare	SR	Forfar
BJ	Suffolk East	DW	Newport (Mon.)	IF	Cork(County)	SS	Haddington
BK	Portsmouth	DX	Ipswich	IH	Donegal	ST	Inverness
BL	Berkshire	DY	Hastings	IJ	Down	SU	Kincardine
BM	Bedfordshire	E	Staffordshire	IK	Dublin	SV	Kinross
BN	Bolton	EA	West Bromwich	IL	Fermanagh	SW	Kirkcudbright
BO	Cardiff	EB	Isle Of Ely	IM	Galway	SX	Linlithgow
BP	Sussex West	EC	Westmorland	IN	Kerry	SY	Midlothian
BR	Sunderland	ED	Warrington	IO	Kildare	T	Devonshire
BS	Orkney	EE	Grimsby	IP	Kilkenny	TI	Limerick (Boro)
BT	Yorkshire (ER)	EF	West Hartlepool	IR	King's County	TS	Dundee (Town C)
BU	Oldham	EH	Hanley	IT	Leitrim	U	Leeds
BW	Oxfordshire	EI	Sligo	IU	Limerick (County)	UI	L'nd'nderry (Boro')
BX	Carmarthenshire	EJ	Cardiganshire	IW	Londonderry (CC)	US	Govan (Town C)
BY	Crovdon	EK	Wigan	IX	Longford	V	Lanark
C	Yorkshire (WR)	EL	Bournemouth	IY	Louth (Ireland)	VS	Greenock (Town C)
CA	Denbighshire	EM	Bootle	IZ	Mayo	W	Sheffield
CB	Blackburn	EN	Bury	J	Durham (County)	WI	Waterford
CC	Carnarvonshire	EO	Barrow-IN-Furness	JI	Tyrone	WS	Leith (Town C)
CD	Brighton	EP	Montgomeryshire	JS	Ross & Cromarty	X	Northumberland
CE	Cambridgeshire	ES	Perth	K	Liverpool	XS	Paisley (Town C)
CF	Suffolk, West	ET	Rotherham	KI	Waterford	Y	Somersetshire
CH	Derby	EU	Breconshire	KS	Roxburgh	YS	Patrick (Town C)

Condition of Discs

The most collectable discs are those with their borders/margins (known as selvedge) remaining intact and in excellent condition.

Early discs had no perforation and therefore selvedge had to be cut away. The best examples (without selvedge) are those that have been carefully cut out.

All discs can be graded according to their condition. Here are the various specifications with examples:-

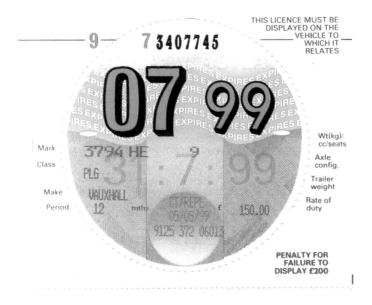

Mint - a disc in 'as new' condition and possibly never actually displayed on a vehicle.

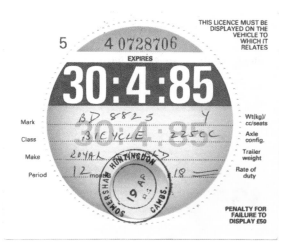

Excellent - a disc that has been displayed on a vehicle, but only shows a minimum (up to 5%) amount of fade/wear. Such a disc will not be torn although if the disc has been removed from its border (selvedge), this will have been performed with approximately 98% perfection.

Very Good - approximately 5% fade allowance but generally no tears or folds and all detail clear.

Good - up to approximately 20% fade/wear. Minor tears around the perforations.

Fair - up to approximately 40% fade/wear. Some tearing allowance but nothing major.

Poor - up to approximately 65% fade/wear. Subject to missing sections but no more than approximately 10% of the entire disc.

Very poor - up to approximately 85% fade/wear. Up to approximately 60% of the disc missing.

BUYING A TAX DISC

The following pages list discs in various conditions. They can be purchased by going to the website www.collecticus.co.uk/auctions or by writing to Trade and Collect, P.O.Box 100, Devizes, SN10 4TE, enclosing the required sum by credit card instruction only. Cheques and Postal Orders are not accepted. All are subject to availability. If any disc(s) you order are not available, your payment will not be taken from the credit card. Please quote the order reference number together with condition and expiry date of the tax disc.

As well as providing an opportunity to purchase, this price list will give you an idea of the state of the market (November 2005).

TAX DISCS FOR SALE

example :- 19861   1923 - A (g)   £100.00

19861 = item no   1923 = year   A = Annual   (g) = Good   £100.00 = Price

Quarterlies :-   M = March   J = June   S = September   D = December

From 1961 onwards :- 1 = January   2 = February   3 = March   etc...

ITEM NO.	DESCRIPTION	PRICE	ITEM NO.	DESCRIPTION	PRICE	ITEM NO.	DESCRIPTION	PRICE
19861	1923 - A (g)	£100.00	19889	1943 - S (f)	£15.00	19917	1956 - A (g)	£6.00
19862	1925 - A (f-g)	£58.00	19890	1943 - A (f-g)	£12.00	19918	1957 - J (g)	£5.00
19863	1926 - A (f)	£35.00	19891	1944 - A (p-f)	£7.00	19919	1957 - S (f)	£2.00
19864	1927 - J (g)	£60.00	19892	1945 - A (p)	£3.00	19920	1957 - D (f)	£2.00
19865	1928 - A (p)	£20.00	19893	1946 - A (g)	£14.00	19921	1957 - A (g)	£5.00
19866	1929 - A (p-f)	£25.00	19894	1947 - J (p)	£6.00	19922	1957 - A (g-v g)	£6.00
19867	1930 - S (g-v g)	£50.00	19895	1948 - A (v p)	£2.00	19923	1958 - S (p-f)	£2.00
19868	1930 - A (p)	£14.00	19896	1948 - A (p)	£3.00	19924	1958 - S (f-g)	£3.00
19869	1931 - A (p)	£14.00	19897	1948 - A (g)	£14.00	19925	1958 - A (p-f)	£2.00
19870	1932 - S (p-f)	£14.00	19898	1949 - S (g)	£16.00	19926	1958 - A (v g)	£6.00
19871	1932 - A (v g)	£48.00	19899	1949 - A (g)	£14.00	19927	1959 - J (p)	£1.00
19872	1933 - M (f-g)	£24.00	19900	1950 - A (f)	£8.00	19928	1959 - J (g-v g)	£5.00
19873	1933 - A (f-g)	£18.00	19901	1950 - A (g)	£10.00	19929	1959 - A (p-f)	£2.00
19874	1935 - J (g-v g)	£32.00	19902	1951 - S (p-f)	£4.00	19930	1959 - A (v g)	£5.00
19875	1935 - M (f-g)	£22.00	19903	1951 - D (g-v g)	£12.00	19931	1960 - S (v g)	£6.00
19876	1935 - A (f)	£16.00	19904	1951 - A (p)	£2.00	19932	1960 - A (p)	£1.00
19877	1936 - J (p-f)	£16.00	19905	1951 - A (g)	£8.00	19933	1960 - A (g)	£4.00
19878	1936 - A (p-f)	£14.00	19906	1952 - J (v g)	£14.00	19934	1960 - A (f)	£3.00
19879	1937 - A (f)	£12.00	19907	1952 - A (e)	£10.00	19935	1961 - 4 (p)	£10.00
19880	1937 - A (f-g)	£16.00	19908	1952 - A (f)	£4.00	19936	1961 - 8 (f)	£12.00
19881	1938 - S (g)	£18.00	19909	1953 - M (v g-e)	£15.00	19937	1961 - 12 (p)	£1.00
19882	1938 - A (f-g)	£15.00	19910	1953 - A (f)	£4.00	19938	1961 - 12 (f-g)	£3.00
19883	1939 - M (p-f)	£14.00	19911	1954 - M (g-v g)	£8.00	19939	1962 - 1 (p)	£2.00
19884	1939 - A (f-g)	£15.00	19912	1954 - A (f)	£4.00	19940	1962 - 12 (v p)	£0.50
19885	1940 - A (g-v g)	£22.00	19913	1955 - J (f-g)	£4.00	19941	1962 - 12 (f)	£3.00
19886	1941 - A (g)	£15.00	19914	1955 - D (f-g)	£5.00	19942	1962 - 12 (g)	£4.00
19887	1942 - J (p-f)	£14.00	19915	1955 - A (g)	£6.00	19943	1963 - 6 (p)	£4.00
19888	1942 - A (f)	£12.00	19916	1956 - J (p-f)	£2.00	19944	1963 - 10 (p-f)	£6.00

ITEM NO.	DESCRIPTION	PRICE	ITEM NO.	DESCRIPTION	PRICE	ITEM NO.	DESCRIPTION	PRICE
19945	1963 - 12 (f)	£3.00	18531	1979 - 03 (g)	£4.00	18431	1986 - 10 (g)	£2.00
19946	1964 - 5 (p)	£4.00	18532	1979 - 03 (g)	£4.00	18432	1987 - 01 (g)	£2.00
19947	1964 - 8 (f)	£7.00	18533	1979 - 04 (g)	£4.00	18433	1987 - 01 (g)	£2.00
19948	1964 - 12 (g)	£5.00	18534	1979 - 06 (g)	£4.00	18434	1987 - 02 (g)	£2.00
19949	1965 - 1 (f)	£3.00	18536	1979 - 07 (g)	£4.00	18435	1987 - 02 (g)	£2.00
19950	1965 - 2 (p)	£5.00	18537	1979 - 07 (g)	£4.00	18436	1987 - 03 (g)	£2.00
19951	1965 - 10 (g)	£10.00	18538	1979 - 07 (g)	£4.00	18437	1987 - 05 (g)	£2.00
19952	1965 - 12 (g)	£4.00	18539	1979 - 07 (g)	£4.00	18438	1987 - 06 (g)	£2.00
19953	1966 - 1 (v p)	£0.20	18540	1979 - 08 (g)	£4.00	18439	1987 - 07 (g)	£2.00
19954	1966 - 7 (p)	£1.00	18541	1979 - 08 (g)	£4.00	18440	1987 - 07 (g)	£2.00
19955	1966 - 9 (f)	£4.00	18595	1979 - 11 (f)	£3.50	18441	1987 - 07 (g)	£2.00
19956	1966 - 12 (v g)	£5.00	18542	1979 - 11 (g)	£4.00	18442	1987 - 07 (g)	£2.00
19957	1967 - 2 (f)	£3.00	18543	1979 - 11 (g)	£4.00	18443	1987 - 08 (g)	£2.00
19958	1967 - 4 (g-v g)	£5.00	18544	1979 - 11 (g)	£4.00	18444	1987 - 09 (g)	£2.00
19959	1967 - 12 (g)	£3.00	18545	1979 - 12 (g)	£4.00	18445	1987 - 12 (g)	£2.00
19960	1968 - 4 (f-g)	£3.00	18546	1979 - 12 (g)	£4.00	18453	1988 - 02 (g)	£2.00
19961	1968 - 6 (f)	£1.00	18378	1980 - 01 (g)	£2.00	18454	1988 - 03 (g)	£2.00
19962	1968 - 8 (p-f)	£0.50	18379	1980 - 02 (g)	£2.00	18446	1988 - 05 (g)	£2.00
19963	1968 - 12 (g-v g)	£4.00	18380	1980 - 02 (g)	£2.00	18447	1988 - 07 (g)	£2.00
19964	1965 - 5 (p)	£0.50	18381	1980 - 03 (g)	£2.00	18448	1988 - 07 (g)	£2.00
19965	1969 - 8 (v g)	£6.00	18382	1980 - 03 (g)	£2.00	18455	1988 - 07 (g)	£2.00
19966	1969 - 9 (p-f)	£1.00	18383	1980 - 05 (g)	£2.00	18449	1988 - 08 (g)	£2.00
18464	1970 - 08 (g)	£4.00	18384	1980 - 07 (g)	£2.00	18456	1988 - 08 (g)	£2.00
18465	1970 - 08 (g)	£4.00	18385	1980 - 07 (g)	£2.00	18450	1988 - 09 (g)	£2.00
18467	1970 - 11 (g)	£4.00	18585	1980 - 09 (f)	£1.50	18451	1988 - 09 (g)	£2.00
18468	1970 - 12 (g)	£4.00	18586	1980 - 11 (f)	£1.50	18452	1988 - 09 (g)	£2.00
18592	1971 - 03 (f)	£3.50	18386	1980 - 11 (g)	£2.00	18457	1988 - 09 (g)	£2.00
18471	1971 - 03 (g)	£4.00	18387	1980 - 11 (g)	£2.00	18458	1988 - 09 (g)	£2.00
18472	1971 - 07 (g)	£4.00	18388	1980 - 12 (g)	£2.00	18459	1988 - 09 (g)	£2.00
18473	1971 - 07 (g)	£4.00	18389	1980 - 12 (g)	£2.00	18460	1988 - 11 (g)	£2.00
18476	1971 - 12 (g)	£4.00	18390	1981 - 02 (g)	£2.00	18461	1988 - 12 (g)	£2.00
18477	1971 - 12 (g)	£4.00	18391	1981 - 02 (g)	£2.00	18561	1990 - 02 (f)	£0.50
18478	1971 - 12 (g)	£4.00	18587	1981 - 03 (f)	£1.50	17977	1990 - 03 (g)	£1.00
18481	1972 - 08 (g)	£4.00	18588	1981 - 05 (f)	£1.50	18562	1990 - 03 (f)	£0.50
18487	1973 - 08 (g)	£4.00	18393	1981 - 05 (g)	£2.00	17979	1990 - 07 (g)	£1.00
18488	1973 - 10 (g)	£4.00	18394	1981 - 05 (g)	£2.00	17981	1990 - 09 (g)	£1.00
18489	1973 - 12 (g)	£4.00	18395	1981 - 08 (g)	£2.00	17982	1990 - 09 (g)	£1.00
18491	1974 - 04 (g)	£4.00	18396	1981 - 10 (g)	£2.00	17983	1990 - 11 (g)	£1.00
18494	1974 - 10 (g)	£4.00	18397	1981 - 10 (g)	£2.00	17986	1991 - 04 (g)	£1.00
18495	1974 - 12 (g)	£4.00	18399	1981 - 11 (g)	£2.00	18563	1991 - 09 (f)	£0.50
18496	1974 - 12 (g)	£4.00	18400	1982 - 02 (g)	£2.00	17987	1991 - 09 (g)	£1.00
18497	1975 - 04 (g)	£4.00	18401	1982 - 04 (g)	£2.00	17988	1991 - 09 (g)	£1.00
18499	1976 - 03 (g)	£4.00	18402	1982 - 04 (g)	£2.00	17989	1991 - 09 (g)	£1.00
18500	1976 - 03 (g)	£4.00	18403	1982 - 05 (g)	£2.00	17991	1992 - 01 (g)	£1.00
18501	1976 - 12 (g)	£4.00	18405	1982 - 10 (g)	£2.00	17994	1992 - 01 (g)	£1.00
18502	1977 - 01 (g)	£4.00	18406	1982 - 11 (g)	£2.00	17995	1992 - 02 (g)	£1.00
18503	1977 - 02 (g)	£4.00	18407	1982 - 11 (g)	£2.00	17997	1992 - 03 (g)	£1.00
18505	1977 - 03 (g)	£4.00	18408	1982 - 11 (g)	£2.00	18564	1992 - 07 (f)	£0.50
18506	1977 - 03 (g)	£4.00	18590	1983 - 11 (f)	£1.50	17998	1992 - 07 (g)	£1.00
18507	1977 - 04 (g)	£4.00	18410	1984 - 01 (g)	£2.00	18565	1992 - 09 (f)	£0.50
18508	1977 - 07 (g)	£4.00	18411	1984 - 03 (g)	£2.00	18000	1992 - 09 (g)	£1.00
18509	1977 - 07 (g)	£4.00	18412	1984 - 04 (g)	£2.00	18002	1992 - 09 (g)	£1.00
18510	1977 - 07 (g)	£4.00	18413	1984 - 08 (g)	£2.00	18003	1992 - 10 (g)	£1.00
18511	1977 - 09 (g)	£4.00	18415	1985 - 02 (g)	£2.00	18005	1993 - 01 (g)	£1.00
18512	1977 - 10 (g)	£4.00	18417	1985 - 07 (g)	£2.00	18006	1993 - 01 (g)	£1.00
18513	1978 - 01 (g)	£4.00	18418	1985 - 08 (g)	£2.00	18566	1993 - 02 (f)	£0.50
18515	1978 - 02 (g)	£4.00	18419	1985 - 08 (g)	£2.00	18009	1993 - 03 (g)	£1.00
18516	1978 - 03 (g)	£4.00	18420	1985 - 10 (g)	£2.00	18010	1993 - 03 (g)	£1.00
18517	1978 - 03 (g)	£4.00	18422	1986 - 02 (g)	£2.00	18012	1993 - 08 (g)	£1.00
18593	1978 - 05 (f)	£3.50	18423	1986 - 02 (g)	£2.00	18013	1993 - 09 (g)	£1.00
18521	1978 - 07 (g)	£4.00	18424	1986 - 03 (g)	£2.00	18014	1993 - 09 (g)	£1.00
18524	1978 - 11 (g)	£4.00	18425	1986 - 04 (g)	£2.00	18016	1993 - 10 (g)	£1.00
18525	1978 - 11 (g)	£4.00	18426	1986 - 05 (g)	£2.00	18018	1993 - 10 (g)	£1.00
18526	1978 - 12 (g)	£4.00	18427	1986 - 07 (g)	£2.00	18025	1994 - 01 (g)	£1.00
18528	1978 - 12 (g)	£4.00	18428	1986 - 07 (g)	£2.00	18026	1994 - 03 (g)	£1.00
18594	1979 - 01 (f)	£3.50	18429	1986 - 07 (g)	£2.00	18027	1994 - 03 (g)	£1.00
18529	1979 - 02 (g)	£4.00	18430	1986 - 08 (g)	£2.00	18028	1994 - 04 (g)	£1.00

ITEM NO.	DESCRIPTION	PRICE	ITEM NO.	DESCRIPTION	PRICE	ITEM NO.	DESCRIPTION	PRICE
18029	1994 - 05 (g)	£1.00	18320	1997 - 06 (g)	£1.00	18598	2000 - 03 (g)	£0.50
18567	1994 - 07 (f)	£0.50	18321	1997 - 07 (g)	£1.00	18599	2000 - 03 (g)	£0.50
18030	1994 - 08 (g)	£1.00	18322	1997 - 07 (g)	£1.00	18600	2000 - 04 (g)	£0.50
18031	1994 - 10 (g)	£1.00	18324	1997 - 07 (g)	£1.00	18601	2000 - 06 (g)	£0.50
18051	1995 - 01 (g)	£1.00	18325	1997 - 07 (g)	£1.00	18602	2000 - 07 (g)	£0.50
18052	1995 - 01 (g)	£1.00	18326	1997 - 07 (g)	£1.00	18603	2000 - 07 (g)	£0.50
18032	1995 - 02 (g)	£1.00	18571	1997 - 08 (f)	£0.50	18604	2000 - 08 (g)	£0.50
18033	1995 - 02 (g)	£1.00	18572	1997 - 08 (f)	£0.50	18605	2000 - 08 (g)	£0.50
18034	1995 - 02 (g)	£1.00	18328	1997 - 08 (g)	£1.00	18606	2000 - 08 (g)	£0.50
18035	1995 - 03 (g)	£1.00	18329	1997 - 08 (g)	£1.00	18607	2000 - 08 (g)	£0.50
18036	1995 - 03 (g)	£1.00	18330	1997 - 08 (g)	£1.00	18608	2000 - 08 (g)	£0.50
18037	1995 - 03 (g)	£1.00	18332	1997 - 08 (g)	£1.00	18609	2000 - 09 (g)	£0.50
18038	1995 - 05 (g)	£1.00	18333	1997 - 09 (g)	£1.00	18610	2000 - 11 (g)	£0.50
18039	1995 - 05 (g)	£1.00	18573	1997 - 10 (f)	£0.50	18611	2000 - 11 (g)	£0.50
18041	1995 - 05 (g)	£1.00	18335	1997 - 10 (g)	£1.00	18612	2001 - 02 (g)	£0.50
18042	1995 - 06 (g)	£1.00	18337	1997 - 10 (g)	£1.00	18613	2001 - 03 (g)	£0.50
18043	1995 - 06 (g)	£1.00	18338	1997 - 10 (g)	£1.00	18614	2001 - 03 (g)	£0.50
18044	1995 - 07 (g)	£1.00	18340	1997 - 10 (g)	£1.00	18615	2001 - 03 (g)	£0.50
18045	1995 - 07 (g)	£1.00	18341	1997 - 10 (g)	£1.00	18616	2001 - 04 (g)	£0.50
18568	1995 - 08 (f)	£0.50	18342	1997 - 11 (g)	£1.00	18617	2001 - 05 (g)	£0.50
18047	1995 - 08 (g)	£1.00	18343	1997 - 11 (g)	£1.00	18618	2001 - 06 (g)	£0.50
18048	1995 - 08 (g)	£1.00	18345	1997 - 11 (g)	£1.00	18619	2001 - 06 (g)	£0.50
18049	1995 - 09 (g)	£1.00	18346	1997 - 12 (g)	£1.00	18620	2001 - 06 (g)	£0.50
18053	1995 - 10 (g)	£1.00	18574	1998 - 01 (f)	£0.50	18621	2001 - 06 (g)	£0.50
18054	1995 - 10 (g)	£1.00	18303	1998 - 01 (g)	£1.00	18622	2001 - 06 (g)	£5.00
18056	1995 - 10 (g)	£1.00	18575	1998 - 02 (f)	£0.50	18623	2001 - 07 (g)	£0.50
18057	1995 - 10 (g)	£1.00	18307	1998 - 03 (g)	£1.00	18624	2001 - 07 (g)	£0.50
18058	1995 - 11 (g)	£1.00	18308	1998 - 03 (g)	£1.00	18625	2001 - 08 (g)	£0.50
18059	1995 - 11 (g)	£1.00	18576	1998 - 04 (f)	£0.50	18626	2001 - 08 (g)	£0.50
18061	1995 - 12 (g)	£1.00	18310	1998 - 04 (g)	£1.00	18627	2001 - 08 (g)	£0.50
18062	1995 - 12 (g)	£1.00	18313	1998 - 05 (g)	£1.00	18628	2001 - 08 (g)	£0.50
18063	1995 - 12 (g)	£1.00	18323	1998 - 05 (g)	£1.00	18629	2001 - 08 (g)	£0.50
18569	1996 - 02 (f)	£0.50	18327	1998 - 06 (g)	£1.00	18630	2001 - 09 (g)	£0.50
18066	1996 - 03 (g)	£1.00	18331	1998 - 06 (g)	£1.00	18631	2001 - 09 (g)	£0.50
18068	1996 - 05 (g)	£1.00	18577	1998 - 07 (f)	£0.50	18632	2001 - 09 (g)	£0.50
18069	1996 - 07 (g)	£1.00	18334	1998 - 07 (g)	£1.00	18633	2001 - 10 (g)	£0.50
18075	1996 - 07 (g)	£1.00	18336	1998 - 07 (g)	£1.00	18634	2001 - 11 (g)	£0.50
18076	1996 - 08 (g)	£1.00	18339	1998 - 08 (g)	£1.00	18635	2001 - 11 (g)	£0.50
18077	1996 - 09 (g)	£1.00	18344	1998 - 09 (g)	£1.00	18636	2001 - 11 (g)	£0.50
18078	1996 - 09 (g)	£1.00	18347	1998 - 09 (g)	£1.00	18637	2001 - 11 (g)	£0.50
18080	1996 - 10 (g)	£1.00	18578	1998 - 10 (f)	£0.50	18638	2001 - 11 (g)	£0.50
18081	1996 - 10 (g)	£1.00	18579	1998 - 11 (f)	£0.50	18639	2001 - 12 (g)	£0.50
18083	1996 - 10 (g)	£1.00	18348	1998 - 11 (g)	£1.00	18640	2002 - 01 (g)	£0.50
18085	1996 - 10 (g)	£1.00	18349	1998 - 11 (g)	£1.00	18641	2002 - 01 (g)	£0.50
18086	1996 - 10 (g)	£1.00	18350	1998 - 12 (g)	£1.00	18642	2002 - 02 (g)	£0.50
18087	1996 - 11 (g)	£1.00	18580	1999 - 01 (f)	£0.50	18643	2002 - 03 (g)	£0.50
18088	1996 - 11 (g)	£1.00	18581	1999 - 01 (f)	£0.50	18644	2002 - 03 (g)	£0.50
18090	1996 - 12 (g)	£1.00	18351	1999 - 03 (g)	£1.00	18645	2002 - 03 (g)	£0.50
18092	1996 - 12 (g)	£1.00	18352	1999 - 03 (g)	£1.00	18646	2002 - 04 (g)	£0.50
18093	1996 - 12 (g)	£1.00	18353	1999 - 04 (g)	£1.00	18647	2002 - 05 (g)	£0.50
18570	1997 - 01 (f)	£0.50	18354	1999 - 04 (g)	£1.00	18648	2002 - 05 (g)	£0.50
18300	1997 - 01 (g)	£1.00	18355	1999 - 04 (g)	£1.00	18649	2002 - 05 (g)	£0.50
18301	1997 - 01 (g)	£1.00	18356	1999 - 05 (g)	£1.00	18650	2002 - 06 (g)	£0.50
18302	1997 - 01 (g)	£1.00	18357	1999 - 06 (g)	£1.00	18651	2002 - 07 (g)	£0.50
18701	1997 - 01 (g)	£0.50	18358	1999 - 07 (g)	£1.00	18652	2002 - 07 (g)	£0.50
18304	1997 - 02 (g)	£1.00	18359	1999 - 07 (g)	£1.00	18653	2002 - 07 (g)	£0.50
18305	1997 - 02 (g)	£1.00	18360	1999 - 07 (g)	£1.00	18654	2002 - 08 (g)	£0.50
18306	1997 - 02 (g)	£1.00	18582	1999 - 08 (f)	£0.50	18655	2002 - 08 (g)	£0.50
18309	1997 - 02 (g)	£1.00	18583	1999 - 08 (f)	£0.50	18656	2002 - 08 (g)	£0.50
18311	1997 - 03 (g)	£1.00	18584	1999 - 09 (f)	£0.50	18657	2002 - 09 (g)	£0.50
18312	1997 - 03 (g)	£1.00	18361	1999 - 09 (g)	£1.00	18658	2002 - 09 (g)	£0.50
18314	1997 - 03 (g)	£1.00	18362	1999 - 09 (g)	£1.00	18659	2002 - 10 (g)	£0.50
18315	1997 - 03 (g)	£1.00	18363	1999 - 09 (g)	£1.00	18660	2002 - 11 (g)	£0.50
18316	1997 - 04 (g)	£1.00	18364	1999 - 11 (g)	£1.00	18661	2002 - 11 (g)	£0.50
18317	1997 - 04 (g)	£1.00	18366	1999 - 12 (g)	£1.00	18662	2002 - 11 (g)	£0.50
18318	1997 - 05 (g)	£1.00	18596	2000 - 02 (g)	£0.50	18663	2002 - 11 (g)	£0.50
18319	1997 - 05 (g)	£1.00	18597	2000 - 02 (g)	£0.00	18664	2002 - 11 (g)	£0.50

TO ADVERTISE IN
TRADE AND COLLECT
TAX DISCS

The page rate for a trade or private advertisement in the next edition of TRADE AND COLLECT TAX DISCS is £400 per page. Half page (£200) and quarter page (£100). Prices are subject to VAT.

Telephone 01380 811760
to register your interest and obtain an idea
of the next publication date.

Alternatively, write to; The Advertisement Manager, Trade
And Collect, P.O.Box 100, Devizes, SN10 4TE

DO YOU HAVE AN OLD TAX DISC FOR SALE?

Send your disc(s) to:

TRADE AND COLLECT,
P.O.Box 100,
Devizes,
Wiltshire,
SN10 4TE

We will send you a cheque in payment. If you are not satisfied with the sum, do not cash it, simply return the cheque and we will return your disc(s).

Year 2000+ minimum quantity 30

Our discs for sale can be found on the internet website:

www.collecticus.co.uk

Notes

Notes